Inversebrates

Inversebrates
Martin Kiszko

Poems by
Martin Kiszko

Illustrations by
Richard Parker Crook

What do invertebrates and poems have in common? Unless we're a zoologist or a poet, we really know so little about either of them!

Well over ninety percent of animals on Earth are invertebrates — millions of species that don't develop or possess a spine. There are also millions of poems around, yet we don't often get to delve into how poetry works. We might know a few poems we read at school, but there's much more about poetry that is challenging, mind-bending, and great fun.

In this collection I'll show you how to compose verse based on poetry forms that have been around for years — but not quite as long as invertebrates have been on our planet!

I hope you'll be fascinated to learn about well-known and not so well-known poetry structures as well as the extraordinary behaviour and characteristics of familiar and not so familiar invertebrates.

Here's an opportunity to brush up your zoology and poetry at the same time. I hope you enjoy *Inversebrates*!

For first-time rhymers and well-versed old timers!

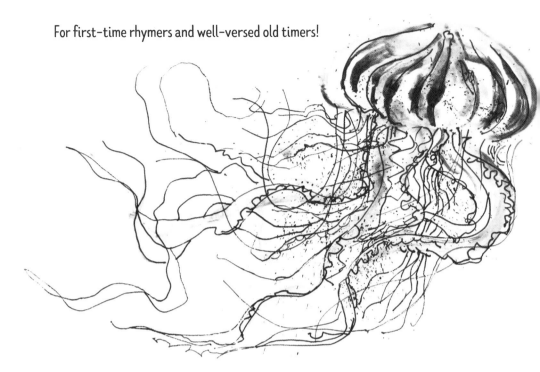

First published in 2021 by Martin Kiszko.
Contact: contact@greenpoemsforablueplanet.com
www.greenpoemsforablueplanet.com
www.martinkiszko.com

ISBN 978-0-9568549-4-0

British Library Cataloguing-in-Publication Data:
A catalogue record for this book is available from
The British Library.

Book design by Simon Bishop.
Typeset in Asegunt and Limes Sans.
Printed in the Czech Republic via Akcent Media.

Contents

Shellebrity Snail is a poem with two quatrains (four-line stanzas) and the rhyme scheme ABCB ABCB. The poem gives a nod to ballad form, though it is much shorter than a conventional ballad which is often a long piece of narrative verse. Ballads began with the wandering minstrels of medieval Europe and are still a part of the poetry and popular songs we hear today.

The poem's humour relies on a neologism. A neologism is a newly invented word and my invented word is 'shellebrity'. I like to think that if my word got into the dictionary, it could be used as a malapropism.

A malapropism is the use of a word that sounds similar to a word one intends to use, but it has a completely different meaning! So, if you said, 'he's a famous complexity' when you meant 'he's a famous celebrity' then that would be a malapropism. The word 'malapropism' has its roots in the play *The Rivals* by Richard Brinsley Sheridan (1751–1816). In the play, character Mrs. Malaprop uses malapropisms.

So, if my neologism did get into the dictionary and I could use 'shellebrity' as a malapropism for 'celebrity', I think I'd be well squeezed! Oops, there goes another malapropism!

Shellebrity Snail

I lived on a backlot in Hollywood,
I crawled around stars on the set,
When 'action' was called I kept it real slow –
No best mollusc award did I get.

My (s)limo dropped me at a restaurant,
Downtown, at the end of my trail.
Didn't dine but was roasted and dined upon,
No movie roles for a shellebrity snail.

Blazon is a French word and is a term that originates in heraldry. It means 'shield' or 'coat-of-arms'. In poetry a blazon is a poem which uses similes, metaphors and hyperboles to praise the physical attributes of a male or female subject — but usually female. This literary device was popularised by the Italian poet Francesco Petrarca (1304–1374). It's a list of all that is beautiful in your lover! Check out the poem *There is a Garden in her Face* by Thomas Campion (1567–1620).

What's more fun is to write an anti-blazon or *contreblazon* which lists all the attributes that might be unattractive or distasteful! Anti-blazons aren't new. Shakespeare wrote one called *My mistress' eyes are nothing like the sun.* I bet she was pleased!

Whilst jellyfish are wonderful creatures, my jellyfish anti-blazon has fun in listing what some might describe as its ugly characteristics. The use of the idiomatic phrase 'you're all mouth' — meaning to talk or brag a lot about something — also seemed fitting to poke humour at one of the jellyfish's main features. Then again, I guess that being able to eat and poo through the mouth is cool!

All Mouth! (A jellyfish anti-blazon)

You're
brainless,
boneless,
eyeless,
heartless,
a tentacled bag
with a mouth!
It swallows your food,
spits out the poo,
squirts out water
to propel you.
And one more thing,
your tentacles sting.
I guess all of that stuff
you brag about
does sum you up —
you are all mouth!

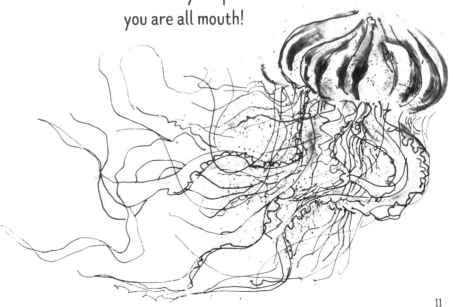

Want to write a haiku? Join the hai-queue! That's all the other poets standing in lines of 5-7-5!

The haiku is a Japanese poetic form. The English version of the poem has three lines composed of seventeen syllables. These are distributed to the lines in a five-seven-five pattern.

The haiku captures a moment in time or aims to create an image or scene in the reader's mind. Traditional haikus usually focus on nature and often include a word that refers to a season. There is also a division in the poem, a point where the poem switches from focusing on one thing and changes to another.

My haiku is about a creature that can live on and on. I guess my reference to nature is the hydra itself, and for my reference to a season I've used the idea of 'old age' as a 'season in life'. My change of focus in the haiku switches from the ideas of old age and cheating death to the celebration of immortality. To emphasise the theme of life going on, my poem is three haikus long!

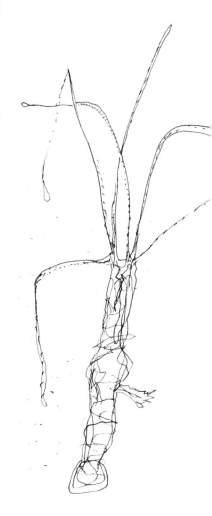

Hydra Haikus

Hydras forever!
Senesce? Not something for me –
I regenerate.

Hydras forever!
Old age doesn't bother me –
I will never die.

Hydras forever!
The years can't catch up with me –
I am immortal.

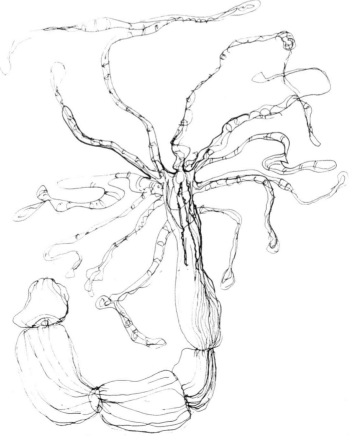

A cinquain is a form of poetry that uses a five-line structure. There are different types of cinquains with lines that employ a different number of syllables. My cinquain is known as a 'didactic cinquain', a simpler form related to the American cinquain developed by poet Adelaide Crapsey (1878–1914). The didactic cinquain is more concerned with the number of words in the poem and their reference to the subject of the poem rather than the use of a specific number of syllables or metre.

The form of the didactic cinquain is as follows: the first line usually names the subject of the poem, the second line uses two adjectives to describe the subject, the third line employs a three-word phrase which describes the subject in more detail, the fourth line has four words that describe the poet's feelings, observation or reaction to the subject, and the final line is one word — usually a synonym (a word that means the same as another word) for the title of the subject given in the poem's first line.

Cinquain for Comb Jellies

Ctenophora:
Bioluminescent, transparent,
Shimmering, drifting, paddling,
Comb-carrying gelatinous sandwiches,
Jellies.

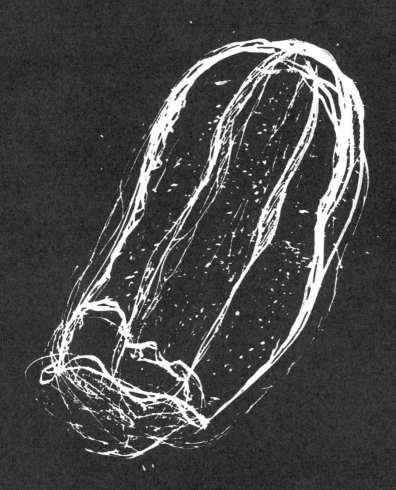

A septet is a seven-line stanza or poem.
My septet is in free verse – it doesn't
adhere to any of the fixed rhyming rules
in septet forms such as the 'rhyme royal'
which was introduced into English by poet
Geoffrey Chaucer (1343–1400). Whilst the
rhyme royal septet is rhyming and often
written in iambic pentameter, a septet can
be rhymed or unrhymed with any line length
and metre chosen by the poet.

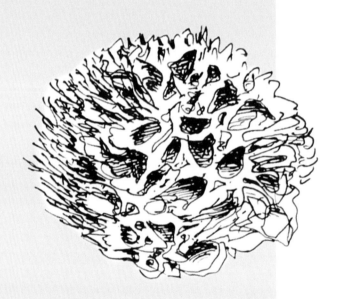

Sponge Septet

I'm a skeletal mass of spongin and spicules,
No tissue, no organs, no nervous system —
I've lots of small pores to allow water flow.
I'm sessile, I'm fixed, attached to a reef.
Who's got my back? No one it seems.
You'll sponge off me
When I'm harvested to scrub your back.

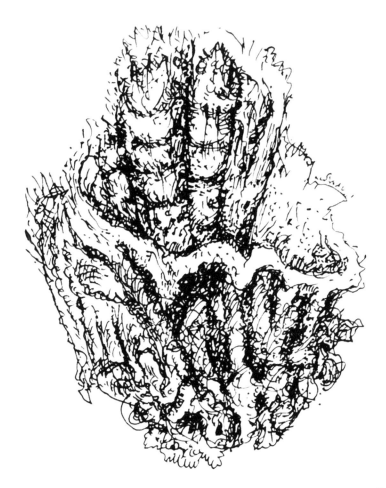

What could be a more appropriate poetry structure to describe an eight-limbed creature than an octave! An octave is a verse form consisting of eight lines. It can be its own poem or a stanza in a much longer poem.

The word octave comes from the Latin word octava which means 'eighth'. There are many types of octaves which have different rhyme schemes and vary the number of syllables per line. The most common rhyme scheme for an octave is ABBA ABBA and the metre is usually in iambic pentameter.

My *Octave for Giant Pacific Octopus*, however, dispenses with rhyme and iambic pentameter. Instead, I've chosen to continue the theme of 'eight' in the poem by making each line octosyllabic (eight) rather than decasyllabic (ten).

It's a pity the octopus didn't have the word 'great' before its name. The title could have included a pun on the word 'great': *Octave for the Greight Giant Pacific Octopus!*

Octave for Giant Pacific Octopus

Eight arms, blue blood, three hearts, nine brains,
Handy for cuddling or crosswords.
Was I the mythical monster
Kraken from the abyssal depths
Or the Akkorokamui,
Sea creature of Shinto folklore?
I'm still around, alive and well,
Living in the North Pacific.

The term 'light romance' is often used to describe a romantic relationship which isn't at a deep or intimate level. I felt the term was well suited to the subject of my poem, first in terms of a poem about two creatures mating and second for its comedic use as the female glows and lets her light lure the male.

The poem is in a free form of my own: AABBCDEFDF, a mix of rhymed and unrhymed lines. The first four lines are made up of two rhyming couplets. The subsequent six lines have unrhymed or rhymed end words.

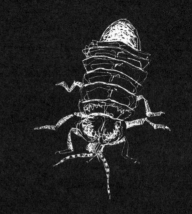

Light Romance

Don't squirm!
This beetle is actually called a worm.
The female doesn't fly but makes her mark
By glowing green in the dark.
Like a steady LED or TV in standby mode,
She can signal to a mate.
He's out late, flying by,
Spots her, comes down low and takes his chance.
That's how glow-worms date.
It's what might be called a 'light romance'.

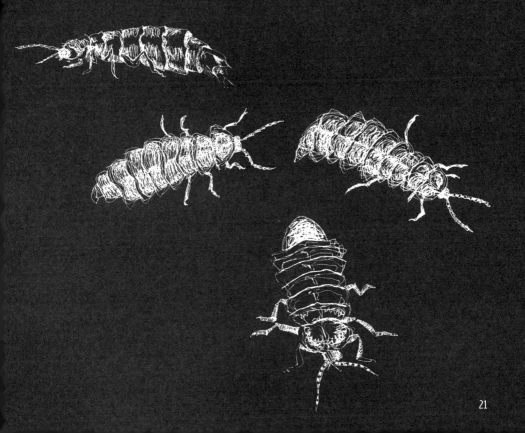

UnBEElievable! tells the story of the rooftop hives of bees that survived the Notre-Dame de Paris cathedral fire in April 2019.

The poem uses six stanzas made up of four-line quatrains of rhyming couplets. This is one of the easiest forms of rhyming poetry to write. Its rhyme scheme is AABB CCDD EEFF etc.

In lines three and four of the second stanza, the word *lady* is used to rhyme with itself. This is known as 'indentical rhyme' and often considered weak usage. However, in each line the word *lady* may be identical but is used to express two different meanings. In line three the reference is to *Our Lady* meaning the cathedral of Notre-Dame as *Notre-Dame* translates from French as ' Our Lady'. In line four of the same stanza the reference to *their lady* is a reference to the queen bee!

UnBE Elievable!

On the roof of ancient Notre Dame,
Above the Seine and Parisians,
Holy bees housed in three hives
Were abuzz at how to save their lives.

As flames climbed walls, roof and spire,
They faced the oncoming raging fire.
Pompiers fought to protect *Our Lady*,
The bees to save queen bee – *their* lady!

If the heat reached sixty-five degrees,
The wax would melt and glue the bees.
Two hundred thousand soon to perish –
A colony so dearly cherished.

The keeper pondered on their plight,
Not one bee was seen in flight,
But images shot from the air
Showed the bees were still up there.

What saved the bees from their fate?
Smoke! Put them in a sleepy state.
Instead of bidding all adieu,
They got knocked out by CO_2!

Later in increasing numbers,
They woke from their sedated slumber
As crowds watched on the miracle
Of what seemed unbeelievable.

This poem began its life as a longer poem of ten stanzas called *Chain Reaction*. The poem described a food chain from starlight to photosynthesis, bugs eating plants, birds eating bugs, rats eating birds, a fox eating ducks. I decided to extract the stanza about bugs eating plants and use it as a stand-alone tercet (a three-line stanza).

As I love changing the sounds of words and therefore their meanings, I couldn't resist turning 'cater' into 'fatter'!

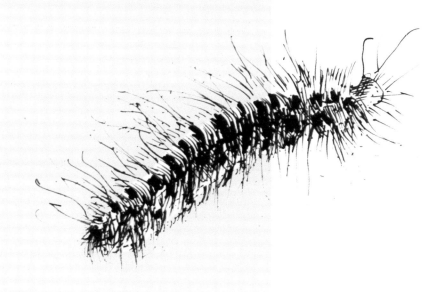

Caterpillars

There once were nettles that grew in the woods.
Caterpillars devoured all that they could.
They're now fatterpillars!

This poem's form is known as a double dactyl. In Victorian times these poems were written as a game or for a bit of fun. But it's not as easy as you think! A dactyl is a word with three syllables such as the word 'poetry'. A double dactyl is two three-syllable words such as 'strawberry poetry'. So, how do you write a double dactyl?

The first line must be two 'nonsense words' of three syllables each. For example, 'higgledy piggledy'. The second line must be 3 + 3 syllables and the name of your poem's character or the poem's subject. The third line must be 3 + 3 syllables and the fourth 3 + 1 syllables.

The fifth line must be 3 + 3 syllables but the sixth line must be one single double dactyl word! That's a word with six syllables such as 'biodegradable'. The seventh line must be 3 + 3 syllables and the eighth line 3 + 1 syllables.

As if that isn't enough, your line four must rhyme with your line eight. Good luck with that!

Double Dactyl for Dragonflies

To, fro, left, right, up, down,
Here be the dragonflies.
Powerful predators.
Insects beware!
My special attribute:
Reproductivity —
I fly in tandem to
Mate in the air.

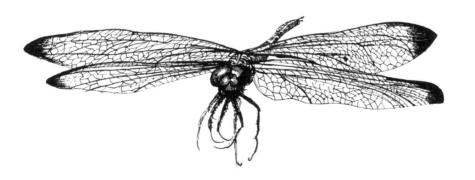

A soliloquy is not typically a poem but a speech that allows a character to express their thoughts without addressing another character. Soliloquies allow characters to make their innermost feelings known to an audience. I felt this was the perfect device for the endangered starfish to connect with the reader or hearer of its poem!

The poem's repeating refrain, 'Give me five, I'm staying alive', gives the poem a sense of pace and rhythm almost like the repetitious lines of a rap. It also connects us with the five arms of the starfish. The ending of the poem with a 'high five' celebrates the final five syllables of 'asteroidea' — the word for the zoological class comprised of starfishes.

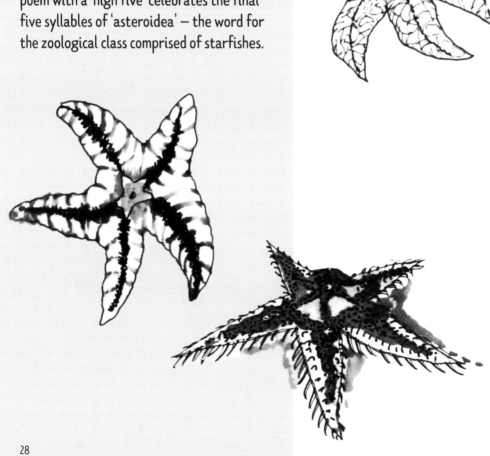

Starfish Soliloquy

Give me five,
I'm staying alive.
I'm not a souvenir for sale
Or a curio for display.
Give me five,
I'm staying alive,
Not in the hands of a collector
Or stuck in an aquarium.
Give me five,
I'm staying alive.
High five,
Asteroidea!

Arachnophobes are not invertebrates but people who suffer from arachnophobia — a fear of spiders. I've chosen to write this poem about their fear in the form of an acrostic.

An acrostic is a poem in which the first letter of each line spells out a word when those letters are read out vertically from top to bottom. The word spelt out can help the reader to memorise the verse. Acrostics can also use the first syllable or first word of each line to communicate a message.

Acrostics were used in medieval literature and even in the Bible.

Acrostic for Arachnophobes

Anxiety,
Racing heart,
A shortness of breath,
Chills and
Hot flushes,
Nausea
Or headaches and
Panic attacks —
Horrendous symptoms
Of arachnophobia.
Best way to cure it?
Exposure to
Spiders!

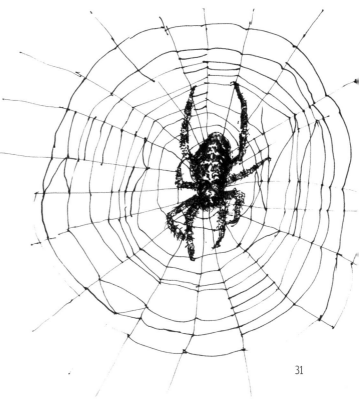

Ballad poetry often portrays dramatic events or tells the tale of a person. In this poem the dramatic tale of the plight of coral is told. The poem is in the traditional form of four-line stanzas with the rhyme scheme ABCB.

One of the challenges of working with scientific or natural history facts is how to communicate the information in verse. When it works, it demonstrates the power of poetry to convey a message succinctly and memorably — information that would otherwise have been lengthy and boring. I was also pleased to be able to pose a question to the reader in the final two lines.

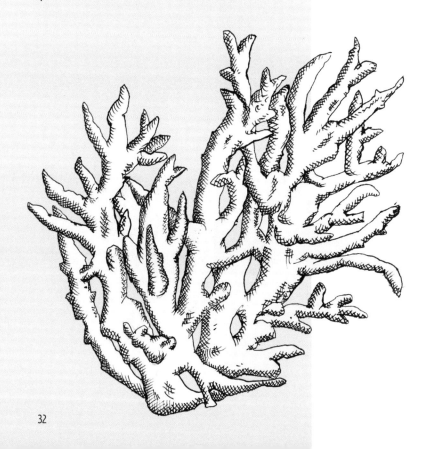

The Moral of the Coral

Zooxanthellae and coral
Have a great relationship:
They complement each other;
They're truly symbiotic.

The algae make their home
In the coral's polyp tissues,
And there they live in harmony
Unless bleaching is an issue.

That's when the water temperature
Of an ocean starts to rise.
The algae are expelled;
The coral bleaches white and dies.

Half the planet's coral
Is in this stressful state.
The reef builder needs our help
Before it is too late.

But what of human beings?
Well this tale does have a moral:
Could we all live hand in hand
Like zooxanthellae and coral?

Once I saw the word 'opera' hiding in the word 'grasshopper', I amused myself with the idea of a poem about a grasshopper as an opera star. I wanted to see if I could describe a grasshopper's behavioural features and appearance with operatic terms. I liked the idea of the creature's stridulation mating song as an aria, its long leaps as balletic jumps, and its camouflage as a costume change.

The poem is in free verse which has no rules in terms of number of lines, metre or rhyme scheme.

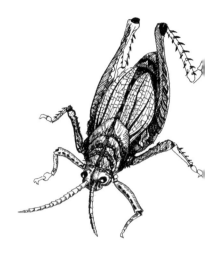

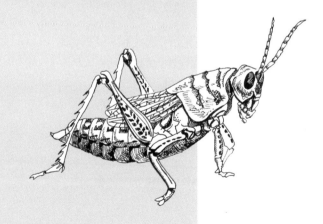

Grasshoppera

In grasshoppera, a hopper has an aria
About a longed-for prima donna.
It's a song performed by stridulation:
Legs rubbed against the forewing veins.

In hoppera ballet interludes,
He performs his grand jetés —
Long-jump leaps
Of twenty body lengths.

His hopperatic role requires a costume change
To twig or leaf or stone —
Camouflage to deter a predator.
Bravo! Bravo!
Applaud the hoppera star!

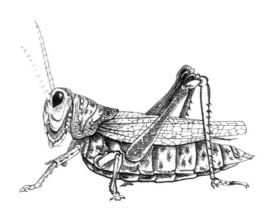

An epigram is a short memorable witty statement. The word comes from the ancient Greek and means 'to inscribe.' The Greeks inscribed their epigrams on the plinths of statues or on tombstones.

These often satirical statements became a form of poetry. The epigram often ended with a line that 'made its point' much like the punch line to a joke. Poets throughout the ages have written epigrams as a single sentence, a couplet, a quatrain or a cinquain.

Epigram for Earthworms

If only the earthworm knew its toil —
Aerates, waters, mixes soil.
What's more its poo is fertiliser.
Darwin called them 'nature's ploughs',
But they're none the wiser.

An epitaph is a species of epigram. It's a
short text or quote which acts as a tribute to
a deceased person. In my poem it's a tribute
to a deceased creature. The word comes from
a Greek word meaning 'funeral oration'. They
can be from one line to a few lines in length.

The Xerces blue was the first butterfly
species to become extinct. Its demise was
caused by loss of habitat due to urban
development. The last butterfly was seen in
the early 1940s near the Golden Gate bridge.

Butterfly Epitaph

Last Xerces blue met its fate
Near San Francisco's Golden Gate.
One more extinct invertebrate.

Like *Sponge Septet* in this collection, *Who's that Lady?* is also a septet. A septet can be a seven-lined stanza or poem. It can be rhymed or unrhymed with any line length and metre chosen by the poet.

The seven-line format is appropriate for this poem as the subject matter discusses the seven spots on the ladybird's elytra and the seven joys and sorrows of the Virgin Mary.

Who's that Lady?

Named after Our Lady —
The mother of Jesus —
Its hard-shelled elytra are red like her cloak.
Mary's seven joys and seven sorrows
Are the seven black spots on its scarlet coat.
So now you have heard in a few words,
Why that cute beetle is called ladybird.

Got it Taped? is a one-stanza poem made up of two rhyming couplets AABB. I decided to give each line ten syllables to keep the flow and rhythm of the lines regular — as if the worm is steadily moving along! It's also a 'concrete poem' as the words are laid out on the page in the shape of the tapeworm.

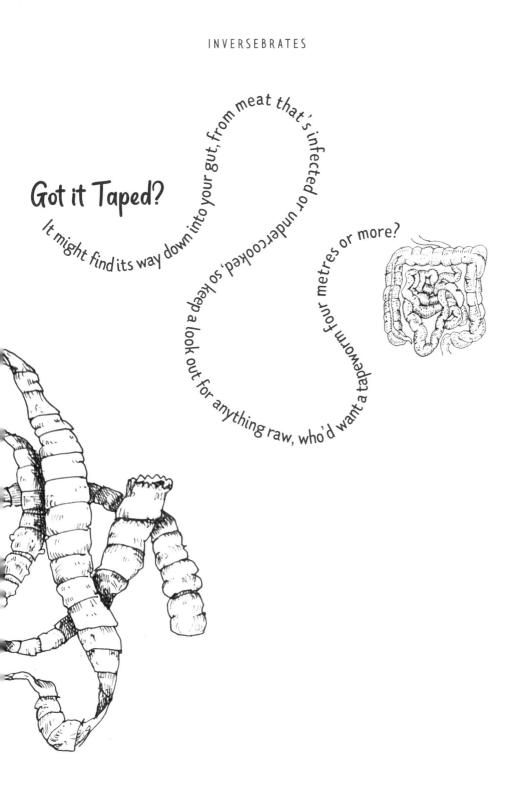

Got it Taped?

It might find its way down into your gut, from meat that's infected or undercooked, so keep a look out for anything raw, who'd want a tapeworm four metres or more?

This poem, based on true facts about a spider named after Beatles band member John Lennon, is a triolet. A triolet stems from medieval French poetry and is a poem with eight lines.

Its rhyme scheme is ABaAabAB. The capital letters here denote lines that are repeated and the lower case letters represent lines that are not repeated. So, the first, fourth and seventh lines are identical (A), as are the second and final lines (B). This makes the first and final couplets identical. Lines three (a), five (a) and six (b) are differently worded lines but share end word rhymes with other lines in the triolet. Trioletmenderous!

Triolet for Tarantula

Bumba lennoni will go far—
Named after Beatle John Lennon.
A Brazilian tarantula,
Bumba lennoni will go far!
With Paul and George and Ringo Starr
Who'll inspire his *Imagine* song,
Bumba lennoni will go far,
Named after Beatle John Lennon!

A footle poem is a very short poem consisting of two lines with only two syllables in each line! It seems a simple task to write a footle but there's also a challenge.

Can you compose an entertaining poem that makes its point with impact and has only four syllables? In my *Fly Swat Footle* the poem aims to be witty – which a footle should be – yet its impact comes with the posing of the question of whether a disease-spreading housefly should live or die.

Fly Swat Footle

Housefly.
Live? Die?

A neologism – which means 'new word' – is a great way to make a poem. I often invent new words to make my poetry more distinctive, comedic or dramatic. Neologisms can be formed by combining nouns and adjectives, by adding a prefix or suffix or by blending words. An example of a blended word is 'brunch' made from 'breakfast' and 'lunch.' Such words are known as portmanteaus.

Words I've invented and often used in poems are wowfabsuperical, specstupentacular, brilltastagorical and coolterrifantical. But that's nothing new. Shakespeare invented over two thousand new words so go for it!

In *Waspitality* I've invented the word 'waspitality' and used it to replace the obvious word that would normally have been there: 'hospitality'. The ensuing result creates humour.

Why not try writing a poem in which you invent your own words?

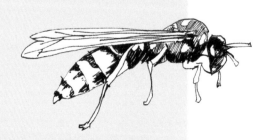

Waspitality

Why can't the wasp return hospitality,
Provide me a feast and show waspitality?
I don't think it knows about conviviality.
This host is devoid of congeniality.

But the wasp gets to come to my dinner dates,
A barbecue, picnic or lunch with my mates.
It's as if I've invited it back to my place
And said, 'Plenty to eat, please take a plate!'
I'm even extremely polite to this pest
As it chooses a space to build a nest
In my garden or house or in my locality —
That's what I call true hospitality.

Can it not get a grip on this reality
And reciprocate with waspitality?
If it can't be friendly and entertain guests,
Could it not expect mine to be at its behest
With their flapping and waving and running away
Or receiving a sting as if they were prey?
This may be a somewhat banal generality
But that's not what I'd call waspitality!

Try a tricube!

A tricube is a form of poetry invented by
American poet and columnist Phillip Larrea.
The tricube's structure has three stanzas.
Each stanza has three lines and each line has
three syllables. It's all about three! There
are no rules about metre or rhyme.

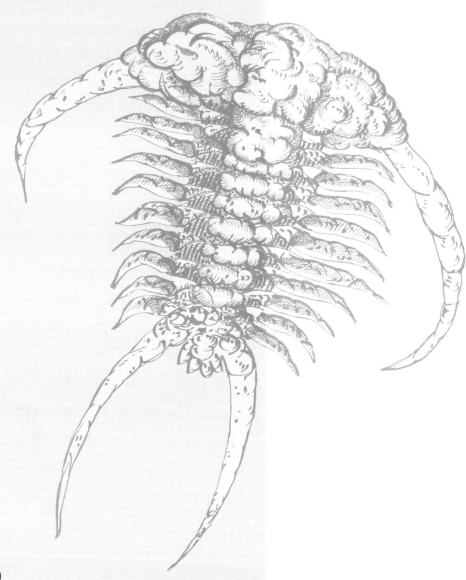

Trilobite Tricube

Trilobites!
You beat the
dinosaurs!

You lived for
three hundred
million years —

until the
Permian
extinction.

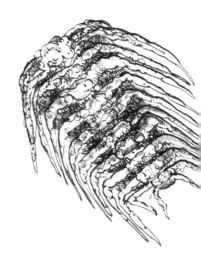

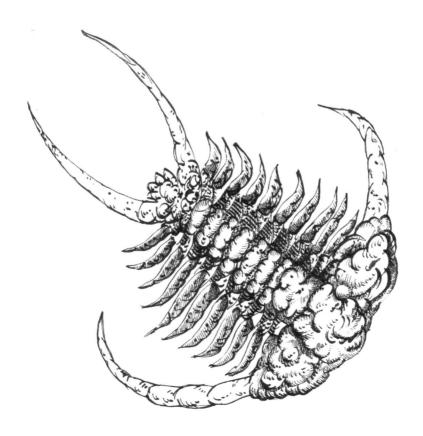

A limerick is a five-line humorous and often rude poem. Its rhyme scheme is AABBA.

Line one, two and five can have between seven and nine syllables whereas lines three and four will have between five and seven. Traditionally, however, the form will be nine syllables for lines one, two and five and six syllables for lines three and four. This is known as 'anapaestic metre' which always has two unstressed syllables before a stressed syllable. So, in this format, the limerick would have three anapaests in lines one, two and five and two anapaests in lines three and four.

The limerick appeared in England in the early eighteenth century and was later popularised by the poet and author Edward Lear (1812–1888) in his *Book of Nonsense* (1846).

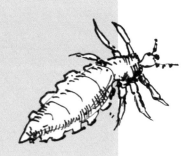

Lousy Limerick

There once was a young blood-sucking louse,
Who took on a boy's scalp as its house.
Then it hijacked his comb,
For a holiday home —
That's a louse with some property nouse!

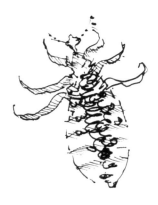

When I was a boy, I collected cards that came with bubble gum. These cards often had short jokes or ridiculous made-up facts on them. They gave me the idea to write *Fantastic Facts*.

I came across the fact that there were no ants on Antarctica and I enjoyed the play of words made possible with 'ants' and 'Antarctica'.

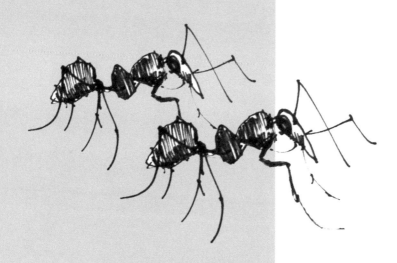

Fantastic Facts

Ants are found on every continent except
Antarctica.
Shouldn't that be the continent of
No*antarctica*?

Although lullabies have helped in rocking babies to sleep for centuries, I thought that a lullaby for bed bugs had been absent in poetry or song for far too long! This lullaby, unlike ones for babies, is not written to create a bond with the bed bug but to get rid of it!

Like most lullabies, the form of the poem is simple and uses rhyming couplets. The syllable count of each line varies but the metre of the poem still allows a rhythmic lilt or rocking motion.

Try it out next time the bedbugs are about. You might discover that they like poetry and are bard bugs!

Lullaby for Bed Bugs

Hushaby bed bugs, goodnight, bye-bye,
Really need my undisturbed eight hours shut-eye.
How about I sing you a lullaby?
'Sleep tight little one till morn is nigh.'
Oh go away bed bugs! Please don't bite.
I can't take another sleepless night.
The itching and scratching is driving me mad,
I must be the best meal you've ever had!
When you've had your fill and my skin turns red,
Why not move along to someone else's bed?
Looking forward to the morning my bad bed-mate,
You'll be in bed bug heaven when I fumigate.

Tardigrades – what amazing tiny creatures. Perhaps there are a few to be found slow-walking through the twenty-two lines of this poem which is written in rhyming couplets: AABBCCDD and so on. There is no particular form to the poem except to say that I decided to give the lines a ten-syllable count to create flow.

Most of the rhyme scheme is in 'perfect rhyme' also known as 'full rhyme' or 'true rhyme.' In perfect rhyme, the first stressed vowel sound in each end-of-line word is identical in terms of its sound. The beginning of the word, however, will start with a different sound. My perfect rhymes in *Tardigrades* are 'more' and 'Thor' or 'worst' 'and 'burst'. The vowel sounds in each pair are similar but the opening consonants are different.

Other rhymes in the poem are imperfect rhymes. They are also known as half-rhymes or slant-rhymes. A word at the end of one line may look a bit like the word at the end of the next line but it won't sound exactly the same. Examples in my poem are 'regions' and 'lichens' and 'lakes' and 'tardigrades'.

Imperfect rhyme is often used because we run out of suitable perfect sounding rhymes in the English language! Imperfect rhyme also helps the writer to get out of the habit of resorting to well-worn obvious rhymes.

Tardigrades

We're known as moss piglets or water bears,
Cute micro-critters with homes everywhere:
Mountains, hot springs, deep sea, polar regions,
Sand dunes, ponds, meadows, mosses and lichens,
Soil and leaf-litter, rainforests and lakes –
We're the 'nothing can touch us' tardigrades.
We super-slow walkers take on much more
Than Batman, Hulk, Wonder Woman or Thor:
Radiation no species could endure,
The extremes of low and high temperatures.
Nothing can faze us so send us your worst!
We can even shrug off gamma-ray bursts.
With low or high pressure we are content.
We'll shun a cosmic extinction event
Or starvation, deprivation of air;
Life without water we easily bear.
Bet you can't do ten years dehydrated,
That's why we're so superhero rated.
What's more we can hang out in outer space.
You might even find us round at your place!
Half a millimetre long water bears –
The hardiest creatures found anywhere.

This type of poem was invented by Edmund Clerihew Bentley (1875-1956) when he was sixteen years old! It's called a *clerihew*! Can you guess why?

A clerihew has simple rules. It is four lines long and the first line has to contain the name of a person. I've used the fiddler crab as my subject. The first and second lines must rhyme and so must the third and fourth. But most of all, the poem must be amusing.

As for the fiddler crab, good job its claw is like a violin and not a double bass!

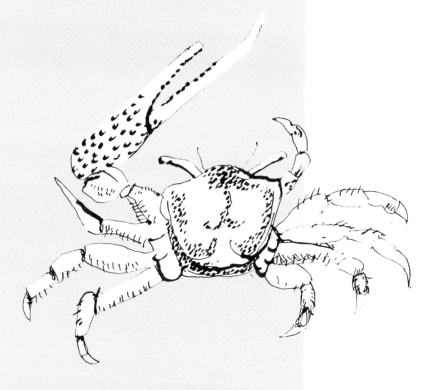

Clerihew for Fiddler Crabs

The fiddler crab has a waving display:
An enlarged claw drives rivals away,
But at his burrow he'll use it to woo a mate in,
As if he were playing a violin.

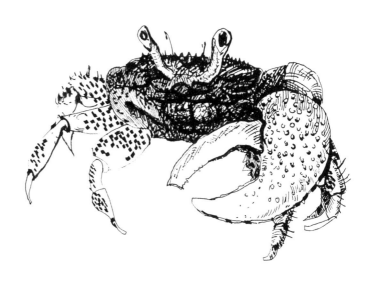

Get your brain into gear — become a sonneteer!

Italian poet Giacomo da Lentini invented the sonnet in the thirteenth century and it was popularised by poet Francesco Petrarca. It is known as the Italian or Petrarchan sonnet and is a popular sonnet form along with the English version known as the Shakespearean sonnet.

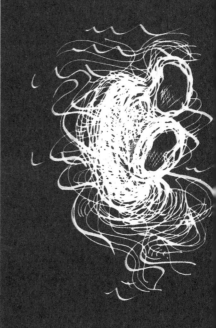

Sonnets have fourteen lines but both these forms differ in structure and rhyme scheme. The Petrarchan sonnet has an octave (eight lines) and a sestet (six lines) with a rhyme scheme ABBAABBACDECDE or ABBAABBACDCDCD, whereas the Shakespearean sonnet has three quatrains (four-line stanzas) and a two-line couplet. Its rhyme scheme is ABABCDCDEFEFGG and it is this pattern I've used.

Sonnets also have a metre. They are written in iambic pentameter — a ten-syllable pattern containing five iambs. An iamb is an unstressed syllable followed by a stressed one. My sonnet adheres to the ten-syllable pattern but doesn't follow a strict pattern of iambs.

It's highly unlikely that Shakespeare got an eyeful of sea squirt whilst penning his poems and plays but he did write many of them during one of the most challenging times in history —the outbreak of bubonic plague. Even the theatres were closed.
Sound familiar?

Sea Squirt Sonnet

Sea squirts start life as tadpole-like larvae.
Looking around for a suitable home,
They land on a shell or somewhere rocky
Or on a ship's hull, the ocean to roam.
A regime for feeding they can't attain,
So have to survive on self-digestion,
Eating their notochord, eye, tail and brain,
A no-brainer for squirt indigestion!
As adults they grow a smooth outer layer:
A useful thick rigid protective frame,
It's known as a tunic — that's their squirtwear.
Tunicate is this creature's other name.
Take one from the sea, be on red alert!
You're likely to get an eyeful of squirt.

An ode is a poem written in praise for a person, a thing, an idea or an event. It was developed in Ancient Greece. There are three types of ode in Ancient Greek poetry: Pindaric, Horatian, and Irregular. My ode is Horatian and the form is attributed to the Roman poet Quintus Horatius Flaccu – commonly known to us as Horace.

The Horatian ode is made up of two or four-line stanzas and all the stanzas have the same pattern. Whatever the poet chooses in terms of number of lines, rhyme scheme or metre for the first verse – all other verses must follow the same pattern.

Horatian odes can be celebratory, meditative, reflective or intimate – hence my reflection on and celebration of the merits of the dung beetle.

I chose to have three stanzas for my ode with a rhyme scheme of AABB and eight syllables for each line. Whether a dung beetle can recite it remains to be seen.

Ode to a Dung Beetle

Since the age of dinosaur dung,
For so many years you have clung
To a ball of animal poo
Much fatter and taller than you.

Ten times your own weight is your ball,
A thousand times more you can haul.
The poop can be used as your feed,
Or a home where you live and breed.

Sacred to ancient Egyptians,
You symbolised the moving sun.
Nowadays your praises aren't sung,
Great roller of huge balls of dung.

Get on it and write a nonet. Quite a brain challenge to write! Start a line with nine syllables and write each successive line with one less syllable until you get down to one! Make the lines rhyme if you want an extra challenge!

The subject matter of the poem is well matched for its form. The nonet dwindles down as each line becomes shorter from nine words down to one — just as my clothing dwindles away as moth larvae eat their way through it!

Nonet for the Common Clothes Moth

Grabbed my jacket for a dinner date.
What's this? Holes in my tuxedo!
Infestation of larvae
of the common clothes moth.
Ate pockets, collar,
sleeves and lapels!
Left me the
buttons.
Thanks.

If you could have a wish to be transformed into an invertebrate (and perhaps one of your ancestors was one!) which one would you choose?

This poem is an englyn cyrch, a Welsh form of poetry. There are many variations of the englyn and they can be found in the work of the earliest Welsh poets. The englyn cyrch can have any number of quatrains (four-line stanzas). Each stanza, whether one or more, has seven syllables per line. Lines one, two, and four must end rhyme with each other. Line three has an end word that must rhyme with the second, third or fourth syllable in line four!

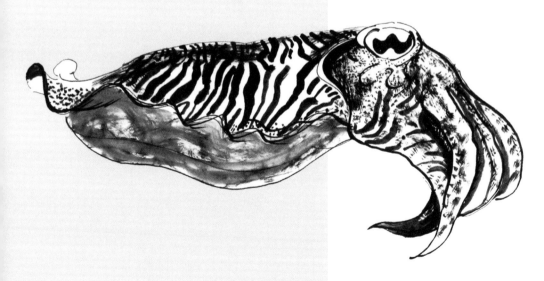

Cuttlefish Wish

If I had a special wish,
I'd become a cuttlefish
With a body store of ink.
Hope you don't think that's oddish!

The ink acts like a smoke screen.
I'd eject it if I'm seen
By approaching enemies.
It's not me that's being mean!

Chameleon of the sea —
Is the name I'd choose for me
As I can change my colour,
Pattern, texture, easily!

Will I ever get my wish?
Or will it simply vanish?
Does this all sound too extreme?
Can but dream of cuttlefish.

Flee flea! is a form of poetry known as a kenning. Kennings were written in Anglo-Saxon times. They are two-word metaphors which describe something without naming it — so they are like riddles. For example, in Anglo-Saxon or Norse poetry a sword might have been called a 'wound-maker' and the sea a 'whale-road'.

My poem is an extended kenning and uses three two-word kennings that have 'referents' — words which describe the flea without naming it! The final word of the poem (as well as the title) names the creature the poem is about — but you wouldn't let the 'cat (or flea) out of the bag' if you were writing a true kenning. You'd want your audience to guess the hidden creature or thing!

My poem also falls into the category of 'concrete poetry' — sometimes referred to as 'visual poetry'. This is where the words on the page create an image or the letters and words visually express an idea. In *Flee Flea!* the words 'high' and 'jumper' are vertically spaced to express the flea's jump, the words 'long' and 'leaper' express the flea's leap, and the downward dripping of the letters of the words 'blood-sucker' signify the bite of the flea.

Flee Flea!

jumper.   Long   —   leaper.

B l o

o

d — sucker.

—

Flee flea!

High

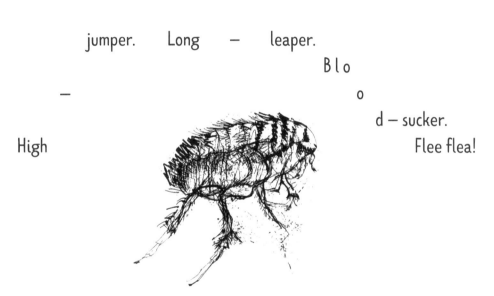

I am Ammonite is a villanelle. The villanelle form is of French origin and appeared in publication as early as 1606 with the poem *J'ay perdu ma Tourterelle* by poet Jean Passerat (1534–1602). Most villanelles, however, have been written in English.

Villanelles have nineteen lines and contain five stanzas of tercets (three lines) and a single stanza which is a quatrain (four lines).

A villanelle has two repeating rhymes and two refrains. A refrain is a line or lines repeated throughout a poem.

In terms of the rhyming scheme, hold on to your hat as the first line of the first stanza serves as the last line of the second and fourth stanzas, and the third line of the first stanza acts as the last line of the third and fifth stanzas.

The rhyme and refrain structure is as follows: A1 b A2, a b A1, a b A2, a b A1, a b A2 a b A1 A2. Letters a and b indicate the two rhyme sounds, A indicates a refrain, and the numerals 1 and 2 indicate refrain 1 and refrain 2.

As for choosing the title, I liked the repetition of the letter 'a' and 'm' in 'am' and 'ammonite' as well as the letter 'i' and 'i' in the words 'I' and 'ammonite'.

I am Ammonite

Entombed in rock, this wasn't my birthright.
Seas were mine for three hundred million years.
Predator of old, I am ammonite.

Back then, the future didn't look so bright.
Now laid to rest in stone, I'm sessile here.
Entombed in rock, this wasn't my birthright.

Three mass extinctions I survived outright,
But with the dinosaurs my end was near.
Predator of old, I am ammonite.

Extinction fell as quickly as the night.
An asteroid veered through our atmosphere.
Entombed in rock, this wasn't my birthright.

More than ten thousand species it did smite,
Until in rock and gem shops we appeared.
Predator of old, I am ammonite.

My coil and sutures catch the morning light.
Hunters approach to take a souvenir.
Entombed in rock, this wasn't my birthright.
Predator of old, I am ammonite.

Centipede is modelled on Hudibrastic verse. Hudibrastic verse is comic verse that exaggerates or mocks heroic qualities. In my poem the heroic qualities of the centipede are in fact true qualities, but whether you'd still want one (or hundreds of them) as your houseguest is up to you!

The term Hudibrastic verse stems from and follows the style of the seventeenth-century poem *Hudibras* by English poet Samuel Butler (1612–1680). Hudibrastic verse has lines of eight syllables as well as rhyming couplets.

The poem is also a 'concrete poem' as it plays with exclamation marks to create the look of a centipede.

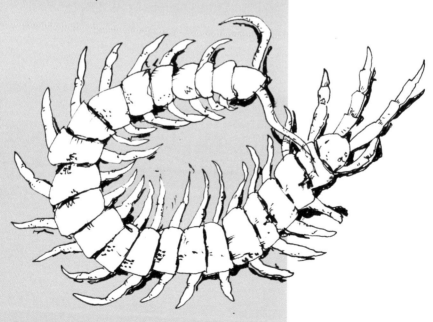

C E N T I P E D E
! ! ! ! ! ! ! ! !

A creepy crawly I'd suggest
!!!!!!!!!!!!!!!!!!!!!!!!!!!!!!!!!

As one a cut above the rest
!!!!!!!!!!!!!!!!!!!!!!!!!!!!!!!!!

Is centipede, by far the best
!!!!!!!!!!!!!!!!!!!!!!!!!!!!!!!!!

Creature to eat your bugs and pests
!!

Or seek out roaches in their nests,
!!!!!!!!!!!!!!!!!!!!!!!!!!!!!!!!!!!!!!!

Flies, termites, moths, it will digest!
!!

As pest control there's no contest,
!!!!!!!!!!!!!!!!!!!!!!!!!!!!!!!!!!!!!!!

Choose centipede as your houseguest.
!!

Whilst six-line poems are often called sestets or sextets, the preferred name is a sexain. What's all the fuss about? Well, sestets are usually defined as the last six lines of a Petrarchan sonnet.

The praying mantis has six legs so I felt it appropriate to give the poem six lines. The poem is also suitably 'prayer-sized' and has three sets of rhyming couplets.

I liked the idea of couplets as they suggest the coupling of the mating mantises.

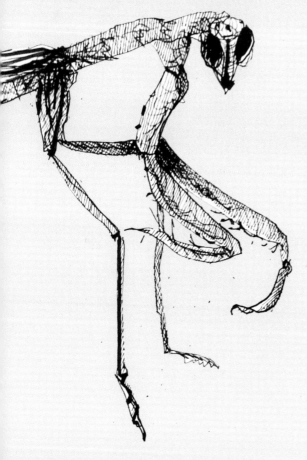

No Praying Mantis

That praying mantis is looking much thinner.
She now fancies me for a slap-up dinner.
If I mate with her, I'm taking a chance.
I'll be part of a decapitation romance.
To have my head gobbled I'd surely lose face.
She won't spare a moment to even say grace.

A tongue-twister is a phrase that the reciter must rapidly articulate and often repeat. Tongue-twisters use rhyme, similar sounding words or alliteration where the same letter occurs at the beginning of successive words. For example, the words 'colossal cephalopod, colossal' in my tongue-twister.

As for 'cephalopod', that's a real word meaning a member of the class of molluscs known as cephalopoda. 'Squidster' is simply one of my neologisms (newly made up words).

Tongue-twisters trip the tongue (there's one!) and create humour as words are mispronounced. They're also a great way to improve your pronunciation.

Colossal Squid
Tongue-Twister Squidster

Call me colossus, colossally big,
A colossal cephalopod, colossal squid.
That's a tongue-twister squidster to twist the tongue,
This colossal squid tongue-twister squidster is done.

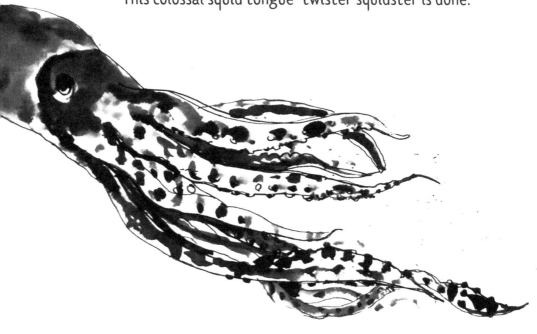

Sea Sheep Rhyme has five stanzas which contain various types of rhyme. There is full rhyme such as 'skills' and 'fill', imperfect rhymes (words that sound similar but are not) such as 'meet' and 'sheep', and identical rhyme such as 'slug' and 'slug' in the first stanza.

It was tricky to communicate the zoology and science through rhyme and it's plain to see that I found no great rhyming possibilities for 'kleptoplasty' (the stealing of chloroplasts from algae by a host organism), 'photosynthesises' (the process of turning light energy into chemical energy), and 'chloroplasts' (organelles found in plants and algae that turn light energy into chemical energy).

Given that the sea sheep is prone to stealing chloroplasts rather than minding its own business, I decided to use the well known biblical idiom of the 'wolf in sheep's clothing' in the poem's final line. The idiom describes someone whose true character is more dangerous than the day to day exterior face of normality they project to the world.

Sea Sheep Rhyme

'Sea sheep', 'sea slug',
'Sheep of the sea',
'Leaf sheep', leaf slug',
Costasiella kuroshimae.

This bioluminescent cutie
Fixes its beady eyes
On the chloroplasts of algae
As they aimlessly float by.

It's a sub-aquatic pirate
With kleptoplasty skills —
Plundering the chloroplasts
To ensure it gets its fill.

It photosynthesises,
For a creature, that's unique —
Making energy from light,
It's solar powered in the deep.

Algae be on the lookout!
Never know who you might meet.
Don't trust those baa-rilliant beady eyes,
'Sea wolf' clothed as 'sea sheep'.

The mondo is a Japanese poetry form comprised of two three-line katautas. A katauta is a three-line poem made of nineteen syllables in the pattern 5-7-7. It looks a bit like a haiku. Katautas are usually about love. My poem could be interpreted as being the subject's love for cocktails — the mosquito's love of blood! It begs a lot of artistic license as a love poem! Nevertheless, it is a mondo.

So, the mondo uses two katautas but the first must ask a question and the second must provide an answer. The question and answer could emanate from one poet or two poets could share a question and answer stanza. The form was once used as training by monks who would pose a poetic question and receive an answer that might contain insight and wisdom.

The mondo also has a similar sister form called a sedoka which is more like a haiku in its sentiments. The first stanza may express or project an image from nature whilst the second stanza would reflect the poet's feelings about the scene.

As for wordplay in the poem, it's obvious that I was inspired by the similarities of the words mosquito and mojito and this was the catalyst for the poem.

Mosquito Mojito Mondo

Why can't I enjoy
My Midsummer Eve's cool drink
Without this gathering swarm?

Forget rum and run.
I'm the sweet cocktail they crave:
The mosquito's mojito.

The ogre-faced spider gets eight lines for this poem to match its eight legs. I liked playing with words and inventing the term 'ogrely excited' which I used to replace the well-known term 'overly excited.'

Ogrely Excited

The ogre-faced spider has gigantic black eyes
Providing night vision for prey it might spy.
To catch an insect it must cast a net —
A rectangular frame spun with its legs,
Which also have 'ears' — sensors at the tips;
If there's quarry behind, the spider backflips.
With such super hearing and being so well-sighted,
No wonder this spider gets ogrely excited.

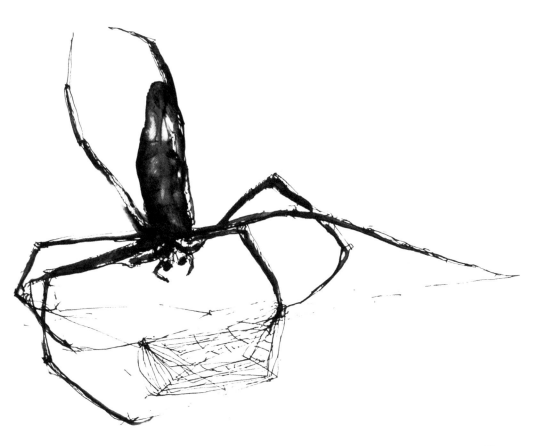

The epulaeryu poem is a form of poetry developed by Dr. Joseph Spence Sr. The word epulaeryu is derived from the Latin word *epulae* meaning banquet, feast or food. Epulaeryus are always about food and usually delicious food. I've taken a bit of poetic license in my epulaeryu. Mine is about food I don't like!

Here is the recipe for writing an epulaeryu:

Preparation.
The epulaeryu can be rhymed or unrhymed. Its structure has seven lines and a total of thirty-three syllables:

Ingredients:
The first line has seven syllables.
The second line has five.
The third line has seven.
The fourth has five.
The fifth line has five.
The sixth has three.
The seventh line has only one syllable.
So, 7/5/7/5/5/3/1

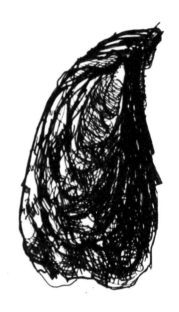

Each line is meant to express the attributes (or in my poem the non-attributes) of the meal. The final word and exclamation mark signifies the writer's excitement about the food.

Go on – dish out your own epulaeryu!
Bon Appoet!

Oyster Epulaeryu

Shall I put you off oysters?
Taste like a rock pool.
Raw ones are eaten alive.
Some say delicious,
To me they are grey
Alien
Slime!

Rannaigheact mhors originated in Ireland. There are different forms but one of the most complicated versions is a worthy challenge for any poet. Want a poetry brain mash? Here we go!

The rannaigheact mhor is made up of quatrains (four-line stanzas). The quatrain must have an ABAB rhyme scheme with heptasyllabic (seven syllables) lines that have consonants as their end sounds.

Each couplet in a quatrain must have a 'cross-rhyme' where the couplet's line one end word rhymes with a word within the couplet's second line. In my first stanza's couplets, mine are 'thing' and 'bloodsucking', 'skin' and 'jaw-dropping'. There are also internal rhymes in each couplet: 'glob' and 'blob', 'gob' and 'job'. Can you spot the cross-rhymes and internal rhymes in the other couplets?

What's more, at least two words in every line must alliterate and the end word of each line four must alliterate with a preceding stressed word! The final word of the poem must rhyme with or echo the first word of the poem.

If you manage to write a rannaigheact mhor without short-circuiting your brain cells, award yourself a prize!

Rannaigheact Mhor for Leeches

What a wormy weird glob thing,
Bold bloodsucking bunched-up blob!
Bladed gob bites into skin —
The leech's jaw-dropping job.

Crackpots claimed they cured disease,
True or tease? Healed diddly-squat!
Lots now seen in surgeries —
Leeches ease congealing clots.

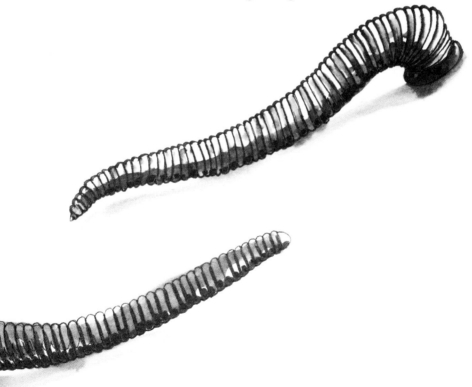

The relationship between the Caribbean monk seal and the mite that lived in its nose seemed ripe for a perfect poetic narrative in the style of Edward Lear's (1812–1888) *The Owl and the Pussycat* (1871). Whilst Lear's poem is regarded as a 'nonsensical' poem, the story in my poem may sound nonsensical but is absolutely true!

Like Lear's poem, I've used rhyme in my stanzas as well as occasional alliteration such as the words 'humans hunt' and 'blood boil.' Another similarity is the use of personification — both my poem and *The Owl and the Pussycat* have the animals speaking as if they are humans.

The Monk Seal and the Nasal Mite

There once was a mite,
A cute parasite.
It lived in the nose of a seal.
A strange habitat,
For a creature like that.
What an odd seal and mite deal.

The seal was endangered,
Likewise the mite.
They often discoursed on their fate.
'If humans hunt you,
What would I do?
I might,' cried the mite, 'lose my mate.'

'Could we be saved?'
The mite asked the seal,
'No chance at all,' the seal said.
'It makes my blood boil,
They're after my oil.
Most of our species are dead.'

'It's bad,' said the mite,
'If that is our plight,
We've teetered right over the brink.
That's how it goes,
When you live in the nose
Of a creature that's going extinct.'

A five-year search was made for the seal.
It ended with no seal in sight.
Caribbean monk seals had gone for good,
So had their nasal mites.

I often think that slugs must think of
themselves as quite smug as they
nonchalantly feast on our vegetables and
plants with gay abandon!

The form of this poem is a terza rima, quite
a challenging structure! The Italian words
terza rima mean 'third rhyme' and the form
was created by Dante Alighieri (1265–1321)
for his long narrative poem *Divine Comedy*
(1320). Geoffrey Chaucer (1343–1400) was
the first English poet to use a terza rima.

Terza rimas use three-line stanzas (tercets)
and 'chain rhyme'– a device that links
stanzas by carrying a rhyme from one
stanza to next. The chain rhyme pattern
of a terza rima is ABA BCB CDC DE. The
poem often ends with the tercet DED and
a final line E or DED plus a rhyming couplet
EE. Terza rimas can have any number of
lines and are usually written in iambic
pentameter.

Be as smug as a slug when you come up with
a terza rima!

Smug Slug

Soft slithery one-footed shell-less slug ,
Must you have designs on my beans and kale?
You are nothing more than a garden thug.

That's right. Don't forget to leave a slime trail
To my well-tended vegetable crop
For more of your troupe to follow your tail.

So, you're back on my beds to window-shop,
But I've beaten you to the strawberries!
Will you get into a sluggardly strop?

I doubt it. You're not going to worry,
You'll head off for my herbs: parsley and dill,
And there you will eat, drink and be merry.

No chance at all of a sluggish standstill,
Looks like my marigolds are your next fill.

I couldn't end this book without inventing my own poetry structure! I call my new form 'sprhyme', a portmanteau word made from the words 'spine' and 'rhyme'.

The sprhyme is a fun poetry puzzle. The aim is to embed the letters of the subject of the poem – in this case the word 'mussel'– as a central spine that runs vertically through the stanza.

The number of lines of the stanza is based on the number of letters in the word that is chosen. There are no rules about metre or rhyme, but for an extra challenge why not have a go at adding a rhyming scheme? You'll require some backbone for that!

Blue Mussel

The blue mussel has Muscles for sure.
When strength is reqUired, it uses its beard to secure
and solidly anchor its Shell to the seafloor.
There it endures the Surge of the waves. Yet, back on the shore,
Seabirds and starfish, Even humans will hustle
For their insatiable filL of the blue mussel.

Martin Kiszko (*Vertebrate*)

Martin studied at Bretton Hall (University of Leeds) and the University of Bristol. He is known as the 'UK's green poet' and has a one-man show based on his books *Green Poems for a Blue Planet* and *Verse for the Earth* – both illustrated by Wallace and Gromit creator Nick Park. Martin has appeared on BBC's *Blue Peter* and Radio 4, and has performed his show from Los Angeles to India, China to Dubai, and Malta to the Edinburgh Fringe. He was poet in residence for Bristol 2015 European Green Capital year and was awarded an honorary doctorate by the University of Bristol for his environmental campaigning and poetry. His autobiography *Major & Minor Adventures in Lah Lah Land* was published in 2020 and his epic eco-poem *King Frank & the Knights of the Ecoquest* was published in 2021 as a book with illustrations by Sarah Vonthron-Laver. It was also broadcast as a fifteen-part drama on Fun Kids radio station. Martin is also a film composer with over 200 film, TV, and concert credits as well as nine albums released with Europe's finest orchestras. www.greenpoemsforablueplanet.com www.martinkiszko.com

Richard Parker Crook (*Vertebrate*)

Richard studied at Preston, Winchester, and Leeds Schools of Art. He was a tutor for seven years at Ashville College, Harrogate, and taught printmaking at York School of Art. He has had one-man exhibitions at galleries in London plus shows at York and Cheltenham Museums. In addition to making a series of paintings for the Salters' Company in collaboration with the interior designer David Hicks, his work has been commissioned for the London Business School, Oxford Business School, Cheltenham College and can also be seen in the collections of Cheltenham Art Gallery & Museum and Longleat House. As well as being a painter and draughtsman, Richard is a wood engraver having made bookplates for the Bodleian Library, Balliol College Oxford, and numerous private clients. Married to the artist PJ Crook, whom he also assists, Richard is preparing the catalogue raisonné on her work; they have two children and two grandchildren. The drawings were made with a Lamy fountain pen and a sable brush.

Acknowledgements

We'd like to thank Simon Bishop for the design, layout and typesetting of *Inversebrates*.
Thanks too to John Garrard and Nick Garrard of Akcent Media Ltd.
Special thanks to my proofreaders Michael Bailey, Jane Jones and Clare Thalmann.